Number Puzzles 1

1. (11) (19) (15)

Use these numbers to complete the equations.

a. **36 –** ☐ **= 25**

b. **48 –** ☐ **= 33**

c. **34 –** ☐ **= 15**

d. **42 –** ☐ **= 27**

2. a. Complete the subtraction table.

–	3	5	9
19			
25			
29			
37			

b. What is the difference between **37 – 5** and **29 – 9**? ☐

3. Take **11** from each of these numbers.

54 ☐

78 ☐

29 ☐

91 ☐

4. Take the **2**nd number from the **1**st in each line.

14 – 6		–
8 – 4		
–	◯	

The final answer is in the circle.

What is it? ☐

5. a. Write the odd numbers between **12** and **24**.

☐ ☐ ☐ ☐ ☐ ☐

b. I think of a number, then subtract **15** from it. The answer is **32**.

What is my number? ☐

6. What might the numbers be to make these sentences correct?

a. **23 –** ◯ **–** ◯ **= 8**

b. **39 –** ◯ **–** ◯ **= 11**

c. **47 –** ◯ **–** ◯ **= 19**

d. **50 –** ◯ **–** ◯ **= 7**

3

Number Puzzles 2

1. **a.** Complete this table, by adding and subtracting from the numbers on the left.

	+5	–9	+12	–20
26	31			
45				
39				19
28				
47				
50				

b. Take the smallest total from the largest total.

Write the equation: ☐ – ☐ = ☐

2. Which operation sign **+** or **–** will make each equation correct?

a. **35** ◯ **16 = 19**

b. **46** ◯ **12 = 58**

c. **26** ◯ **11 = 15**

d. **18** ◯ **28 = 46**

e. **59** ◯ **30 = 29**

3. Fill in the numbers so that each row makes 46.

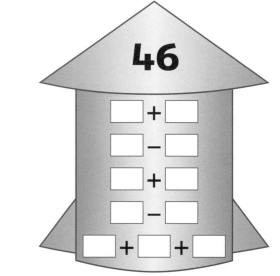

Animals

1. Pajeet found **12** ladybirds.
Each one had **3** spots.

   a. How many spots were there?

   ☐ spots

   b. If **6** ladybirds flew away how many
   spots would there be then?

   ☐ spots

2. Each butterfly has **2** antennae.

   a. In the butterfly house we saw
   33 butterflies.
   How many antennae were there?

   ☐ antennae

   b. If these were joined by another
   33 butterflies, how many antennae
   would there be then? ☐

3. Ria could see **16** pairs of eyes staring
at her.

   a. How many eyes were there?

   ☐ eyes

   b. How many more monkeys came
   to make a total of **50** eyes?

   ☐ monkeys

4. Bert checked his **12** cows' hooves.

   a. How many hooves did he check?

   ☐ hooves

   b. How many hooves did Bert check
   in the next field of **10** cows?

   ☐ hooves

Multiples

1. **a.** Circle the multiples of **2**.

18	19	20	7
27	13	14	29
16	15	17	36
42	31	12	8

b. Write some multiples of **4**.

2. Tall Todd is lassoing multiples of **10**. Write them in the lasso.

20	100	46	40	82	93	61	33
50	29	57	48	60	73	24	26
80	84	70	30	77	39	99	90

3. Cheerful Chad is lassoing multiples of **5**. Write them in the lasso.

15	8	23	12	17	47	45
30	36	29	10	25	43	50
42	35	13	20	26	40	38

4. **a.** Circle the multiples of **3**.

15	10	1	9
8	12	6	30
7	19	18	21
26	36	27	24

b. Write some multiples of **6**.

Lines of symmetry

1. Colour the letters with **no** lines of symmetry.

F D S C T G

2. Draw **4** lines of symmetry on the flag.

3. Draw **2** lines of symmetry on the rectangle.

4. Colour the numbers with lines of symmetry.

3 7 1 5 8

5. Complete the picture showing the line of symmetry.

6. Draw the lines of symmetry.

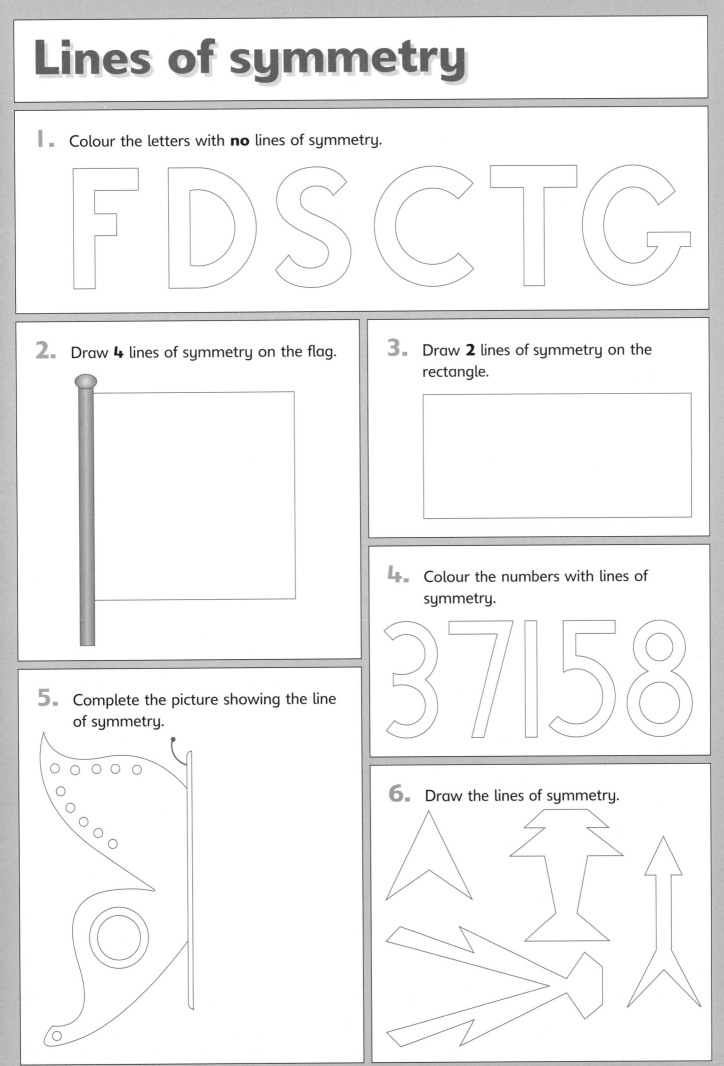

Money

1. Show **6** ways to make **50**p. The first one is done for you.

	1p	2p	5p	10p	20p	50p	£1
1			2	4			
2							
3							
4							
5							
6							

2. Now, show **6** ways to make £**1**.

	1p	2p	5p	10p	20p	50p	£1
1							
2							
3							
4							
5							
6							

Number Puzzles 3

1. **a.** Add the numbers in a straight line. The arrows will help you.

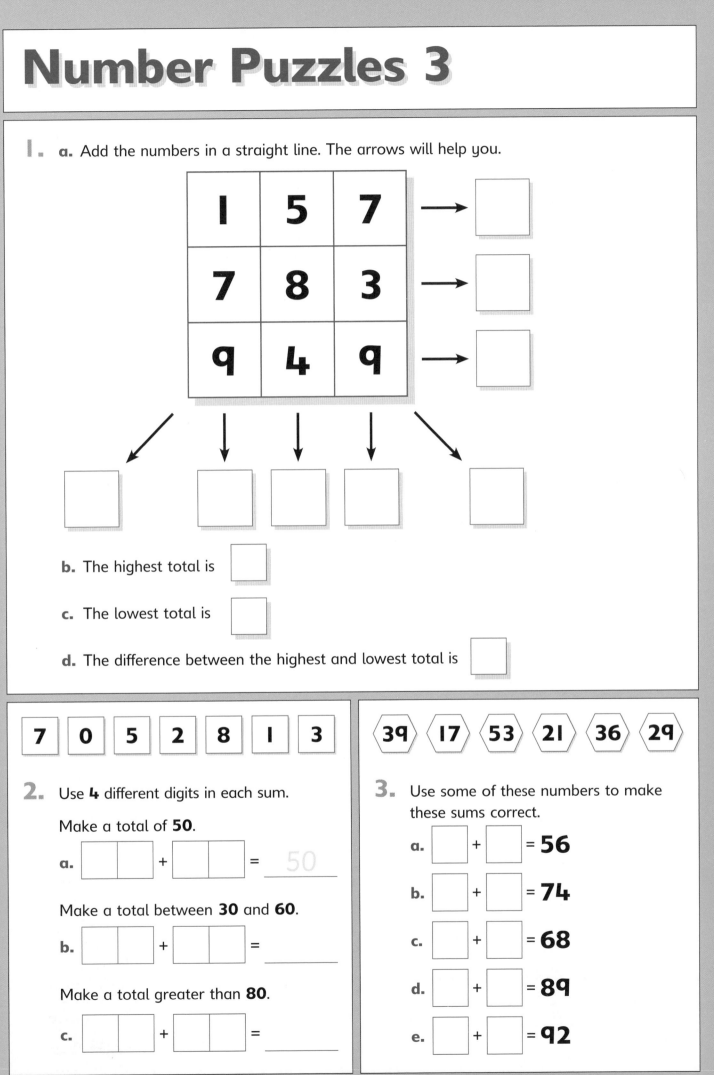

1	5	7
7	8	3
9	4	9

b. The highest total is ☐

c. The lowest total is ☐

d. The difference between the highest and lowest total is ☐

| 7 | 0 | 5 | 2 | 8 | 1 | 3 |

2. Use **4** different digits in each sum.

   Make a total of **50**.

   a. ☐☐ + ☐☐ = 50

   Make a total between **30** and **60**.

   b. ☐☐ + ☐☐ = ___

   Make a total greater than **80**.

   c. ☐☐ + ☐☐ = ___

⬡39 ⬡17 ⬡53 ⬡21 ⬡36 ⬡29

3. Use some of these numbers to make these sums correct.

   a. ☐ + ☐ = **56**

   b. ☐ + ☐ = **74**

   c. ☐ + ☐ = **68**

   d. ☐ + ☐ = **89**

   e. ☐ + ☐ = **92**

Linear Measurement

1.

Dad mowed the lawn in stripes.
Each stripe was **4** metres long.
He mowed **10** stripes. How many
metres did he mow?

[ ] m

2.

A giraffe can reach
to **12** metres but the
tree is **18** metres
high. How much
taller is the tree than
the giraffe?

[ ] m taller

3.

The hedge is **2** metres high.
The garage roof is twice as high
as the hedge. How high is the
garage roof?

[ ] m high

4.

The garden is **18** metres wide.
Mum wants her washing line to
stretch from one side to the other,
but she has only a **3** metre length.
How much more washing line does
she need?

[ ] m more

5.

Mum bought
25 metres of
material for
some curtains.
She cut it in half
to make two
curtains the
same size. What
length did she
need for each
curtain?

[ ] m

6. A bookcase has
5 shelves. The
shelves are each
2 centimetres
thick. The gaps
between the
shelves are each
30 centimetres.
How tall is the
bookcase?

[ ] cm

Year 3's Favourite Stories

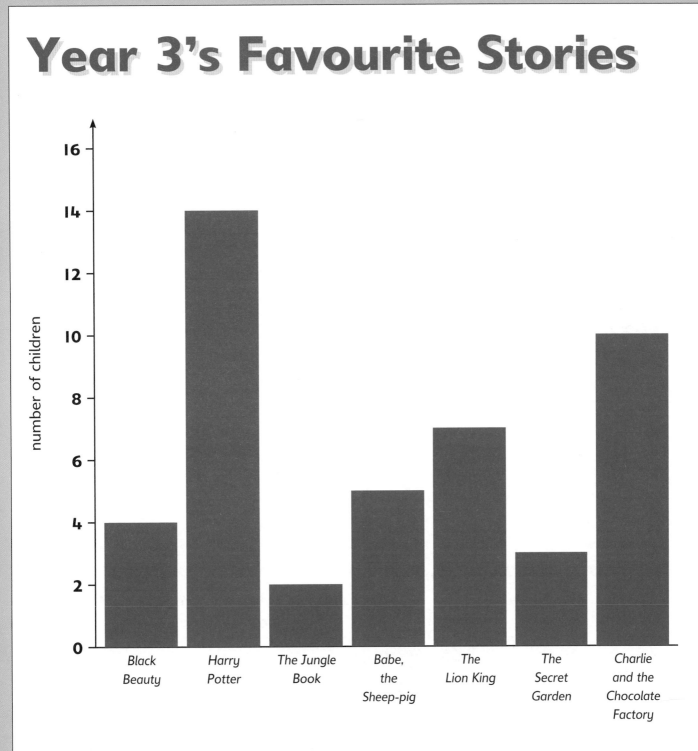

1. Which is the most popular story in Year 3? _____

2. Which is the least popular story in Year 3? _____

3. How many more children prefer *The Lion King* to *The Jungle Book*? ☐

4. How many fewer children prefer *Babe, the Sheep-pig* to *Charlie and the Chocolate Factory*? ☐

5. Which story do you think is the most popular with boys? _____

   with girls? _____

6. How many children in Year 3 read these stories? ☐

Capacity

1. This juice bottle holds **2** litres.

    a. How much will **10** bottles hold?

                    [l]

    b. George drinks half a bottle of juice. How much is left in the bottle?

                    [l]

2. A baby's bottle holds **250**ml of milk.

    a. How much milk is needed altogether for one feed for the twins?

        [ml] milk

    b. The twins are fed **3** times a day. How much milk is needed each day?

        [ml] milk

3. Dad bought **30** litres of petrol. He used **9** litres to go to work.

    a. How many litres were left?

        [l]

    b. By the time he gets home he has used double the amount. How much is left then?

        [l]

4. Jed takes two **5**ml spoonsful of cough mixture after breakfast.

    a. How much cough mixture does he take?

        [ml]

    b. He takes this amount **3** times a day. How much does he take?

        [ml]

    c. In a week he takes [ml]

Balloons

1. Henry bought **3** Jet balloons for his friends.

   How much did the balloons cost?

2. Pippa has two **50**p coins, two **10**p coins and one **5**p coin. She pays £1.15 for balloons.

   a. How much money did she have left?

   b. Which balloons do you think she bought? _____

3. Zara buys **10** animal balloons for her party.

   a. How much did she pay in total?

   b. She had a £**5.00** note.
   What were the three silver coins she was given for change?

4. Scarlett buys **5** round balloons and a jet balloon for her brother using a £**2** coin.

   a. How much does she pay?

   b. Which one coin is she given for her change?

5. If you had £**8.00** to spend on balloons,

   a. Which would you buy? _____

   _____

   b. Would you have any change? _____

   c. If so, how much?

13

Number Puzzles 4

1. **a.** 10 times ☐ add **7** is **57**

b. **5** times ☐ add **9** is **39**

c. **2** times ☐ add **6** is **56**

d. **4** times ☐ add **3** is **23**

e. Double ☐ add **5** is **45**

f. Write one of your own.

☐ times ☐ add ☐ is ☐

2. Write the multiple of **10**

a. before **40** ☐

b. after **50** ☐

c. between **70** and **90** ☐

d. closest to **106** ☐

e. Write one of your own. ☐

3. This is part of a **100** square. Fill in the missing numbers.

2	3	4		
		14		
22				
		34		

4. **a.** What position is the 3rd ■ bead?

○-○-○-■-○-○-○-■-○-○-○-■-○-○-○-■-○-○-○

☐

b. What position is the 4th ● bead?

●-☐-☐-☐-☐-●-☐-☐-☐-☐-●-☐-☐-☐-☐-●-☐-☐-☐-☐-●

☐

5. Multiply one of the numbers on the dice by **4** to give a number greater than **18** but less than **24**. ☐

6. Daisy thought of a number. She doubled it and added **5**. The answer was **45**.

a. What was the number she thought of? ☐

b. Now think of your own number. ☐

Double it! ☐

Add **5**. ☐

Pull-out Answers

Page 3

1. a. 11
   b. 15
   c. 19
   d. 15

2. a.

16	14	10
22	20	16
26	24	20
34	32	28

   b. 12

3. 43, 67, 18, 80

4. Final answer = 4

5. a. 13, 15, 17,
      19, 21, 23
   b. 47

6. A variety of answers
   for each part.

Page 4

1. a.

31	17	38	6
50	36	57	25
44	30	51	19
33	19	40	8
52	38	59	27
55	41	62	30

   b. 62 – 6 = 56

2. a. – b. + c. –
   d. + e. –

3. A variety of possible
   answers.

Page 5

1. a. 36
   b. 18

2. a. 66
   b. 132

3. a. 32
   b. 9

4. a. 48
   b. 40

Page 6

1. a. 18, 20, 14,
      16, 36, 42,
      12, 8 circled
   b. Any multiples of 4
      e.g. 4, 8, 12, 16, 20,
      24, 28, 32 ... etc.

2. 20, 30, 40, 50, 60,
   70, 80, 90, 100.

3. 10, 15, 20, 25, 30,
   35, 40, 45, 50

4. a. 15, 9, 12, 6, 30, 18,
      21, 36, 27, 24 circled

   b. Any multiples of 6
      e.g. 6, 12, 18, 24, 30,
      36, 42, 48, 54, 60
      ... etc.

Page 7

1. **F, S,** and **G** coloured

2. 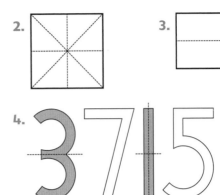 3.

4.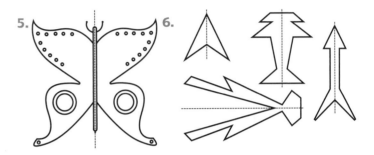

5. 6.

Page 8

1. A variety of answers in any order, e.g.

1p	2p	5p	10p	20p	50p	£1
		2	4			
			5			
					1	
50						
		2		2		
10	5	2		1		

2. A variety of answers in any order, e.g.

1p	2p	5p	10p	20p	50p	£1
			10			
			2	4		
	5	2	1	1	1	
						1
20	10	4	2	1		
5	5	1	1	1	1	

A1

Page 9

1. a.
```
  1  5  7 → 13
  7  8  3 → 18
  9  4  9 → 22
  ↙  ↓  ↓  ↓  ↘
 24 17 17 19  18
```
   b. **24**
   c. **13**
   d. **11**

2. A variety of
   answers for each
   part,
   a. e.g. **18 + 32 = 50**
   b. e.g. **37 + 21 = 58**
   c. e.g. **75 + 23 = 98**

3. a. **39 + 17** or **17 + 39**
   b. **53 + 21** or **21 + 53**
   c. **39 + 29** or **29 + 39**
   d. **53 + 36** or **36 + 53**
   e. **39 + 53** or **53 + 39**

Page 10

1. **40m**
2. **6m**
3. **4m**
4. **15m**
5. **12.5** or **12½m**
6. **162m**

Page 11

1. Harry Potter
2. The Jungle Book
3. **5**
4. **5**
5. Answers require an opinion.
6. **45**

Page 12

1. a. **20 litres**
   b. **1 litre**

2. a. **500ml**
   b. **1500ml**

3. a. **21 litres**
   b. **12 litres**

4. a. **10ml**
   b. **30ml**
   c. **210ml**

Page 13

1. **£1.50**
2. a. **10p**
   b. several possible answers e.g.
      1 animal, **1** jet, **1** round or
      2 animals, **1** oval ...
3. a. **£4.50**
   b. **20p, 20p 10p**
4. a. **£1.50**
   b. **50p** coin
5. A variety of answers based on the child's choices.

Page 14

1. a. **5**
   b. **6**
   c. **25**
   d. **5**
   e. **20**
   f. various

2. a. **30**
   b. **60**
   c. **80**
   d. **110**
   e. various

3.
```
 2  3  4
   13 14        18
22 23      27
   33 34 35 36
      44
      54
```

4. a. **12th**
   b. **16th**

5. **20**

6. a. **20**
   b. various

Page 15

1. **25**
2. a. **18**
   b. **6**
3. a. **34**
   b. **17**
4. a. **50**
   b. **75**
   c. **75**

Page 16

1.
   ½ past 4

2.
   20 past 5

3.
   2 ½ hours

4.
   20 minutes

Page 17

5. **200g** margarine
   120g sugar
   2 tablespoons syrup
   300g oats

6.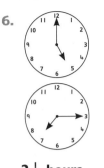

   2¼ hours

7. a.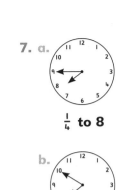

   ¼ to 8

   b.

   10 to 8

   c.

   20 to 8

8.

   b. **½ past 8**

9. a. **16**
   b. **8**

Page 18

1. a. **£15**
   b. **£30**

2. a. **£5.90**
   b. **2**

3. a. **£8.65**
   b. **865p**

4. a. **96p**
   b. **£5.76**
   c. **24p**

Page 19

1. **Marcus:** 2·00
              + 1·00
              ─────
              £ 3·00

2. **Emily:**   1.80
                  50
               ─────
               £ 2.30

3. **Isabelle:**   90
               +   80
               ─────
               £ 1.70

4. Various

Page 20

1. cars
2. **30** buses
3. **12** more
4. **176**
5. Friday
6. There are always more cars on the road than coaches. More people use cars.
7. Snow plough or Gritting lorry.

Page 21

1. a.

25	31	22
23	26	29
30	21	27

12	17	10
11	13	15
16	9	14

   b. Check that each row, column and diagonal add up to the same number

2.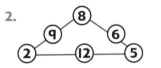

3. a. **100**
   b. **96**
   c. **378**

4. a. **25**
   b. **18**
   c. **63**
   d. **54**
   e. **85**

5. **35** joined to **20**
   41 joined to **26**
   66 joined to **81**
   32 joined to **47**
   79 joined to **64**

Page 22

1. a. Robert the Robot
   b. News
   c. Winnie the Pooh
   d. The Big Blue Bus
   e. Robin Hood

2. a. **30** minutes or **½** an hour
   b. **25** minutes
   c. **10** minutes
   d. **1½** hours or **90** minutes
   e. **5** minutes
   f. **25** minutes
   g. **30** minutes or **½** an hour
   h. **15** minutes or **¼** of an hour

Page 23

3. Rumbles and The Tinkers
4. Sophie and Sam, and The Tinkers
5. **2** hours
6. a. b. c. d. e.

7. Any selection of programmes which total **90** minutes
8. Various answers

Page 24

1. a. **15** days
   b. Thursday
   c. **3** hours

2. a. **£12.00**
   b. **45**
   c. **15**

3. a. **30**
   b. **14**

4. a. **15**
   b. **£22.50**

5. a. **76**
   b. **19**

Page 25

6. a. Circle and cone
   b. Circle and cylinder

7.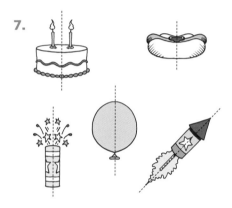

8. a. **7:50** or **10 to 8**

9. **32**

10. **24**

11. **91**

Page 26

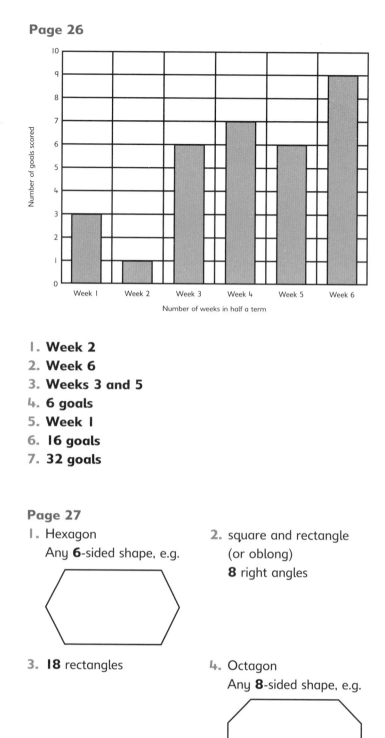

1. **Week 2**
2. **Week 6**
3. **Weeks 3 and 5**
4. **6 goals**
5. **Week 1**
6. **16 goals**
7. **32 goals**

Page 27

1. Hexagon
   Any **6**-sided shape, e.g.

2. square and rectangle
   (or oblong)
   8 right angles

3. **18** rectangles

4. Octagon
   Any **8**-sided shape, e.g.

5. **30** squares

6. **8** triangles

In the Garden

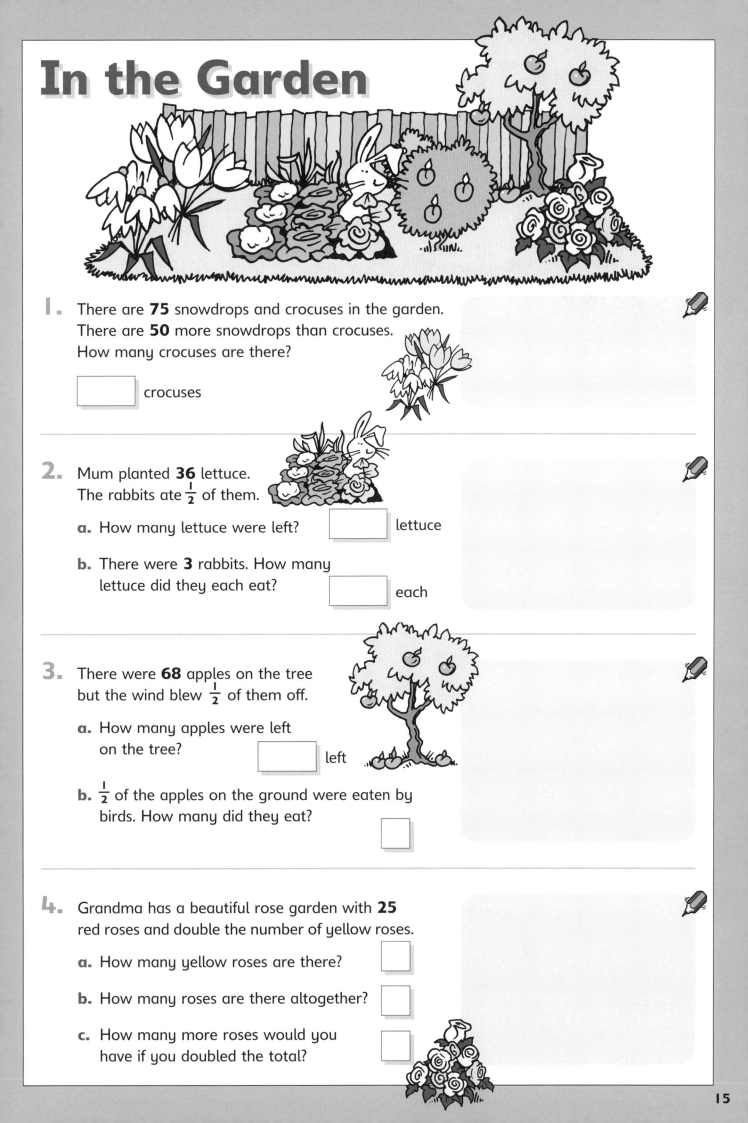

1. There are **75** snowdrops and crocuses in the garden.
   There are **50** more snowdrops than crocuses.
   How many crocuses are there?

   ☐ crocuses

2. Mum planted **36** lettuce.
   The rabbits ate $\frac{1}{2}$ of them.

   a. How many lettuce were left? ☐ lettuce

   b. There were **3** rabbits. How many
      lettuce did they each eat? ☐ each

3. There were **68** apples on the tree
   but the wind blew $\frac{1}{2}$ of them off.

   a. How many apples were left
      on the tree? ☐ left

   b. $\frac{1}{2}$ of the apples on the ground were eaten by
      birds. How many did they eat?
      ☐

4. Grandma has a beautiful rose garden with **25**
   red roses and double the number of yellow roses.

   a. How many yellow roses are there? ☐

   b. How many roses are there altogether? ☐

   c. How many more roses would you
      have if you doubled the total? ☐

Supper Time

1. Mum and Tom had **3** hours to cook supper before Dad came home at $\frac{1}{2}$ past **7**.

What time did they start cooking?

They started cooking at _____

2. It took Tom **5** minutes to peel the potatoes. He started peeling at $\frac{1}{4}$ past **5**.

He finished peeling at _____

3. The chicken casserole went in the hot oven at **5** o'clock for **30** minutes. Then it cooked for **2** hours in a slow oven.

How long did it take to cook?

It took _____ to cook.

4. The carrots started cooking at **7.10**p.m. They were ready at **7.30**p.m.

How long did it take to cook them?

It took _____ to cook.

Flapjacks

100g margarine
60g sugar
1 tablespoon syrup
150g oats

Oven **350**°F/**180**°C
Gas mark **4**

1. Weigh and measure the first **3** ingredients.
2. Put in a pan and heat until sugar melts.
3. Weigh oats and add to pan.
4. Mix well.
5. Bake for **30** minutes.
6. Cut into pieces while warm. Turn out when cold.

5. **Read the recipe**
Change the amounts of the ingredients to make double the quantity.

[ ] g margarine

[ ] g sugar

[ ] g tablespoons syrup

[ ] g oats

6. Mum put a rice pudding in the oven at **5** o'clock and took it out at ¼ past **7**.

How long did it take to cook?

_____

7. The family started supper at **7.30**p.m. It took Dad **15** minutes to eat, Mum **20** minutes and Tom **10** minutes. Show the time each finished on the clocks.

a.   **b.**   **c.**

Dad finished at _____

Mum finished at _____

Tom finished at _____

8. After supper Dad read his post until **8**p.m. Then it took him **5** minutes to clear the table. Then the phone rang, he spoke to his friend for **10** minutes and then washed up for **15** minutes.

He then sat down to watch TV.

What time did he start to watch TV?

_____

9. After supper Tom made flapjacks using the recipe at the top of the page. After it was cooked he cut it into **4** rows across and **4** rows down.

a. How many pieces were there?

[ ] pieces

b. Half of the flapjacks were put into a tin. How much was left for the family to eat?

[ ] pieces

Money Boxes

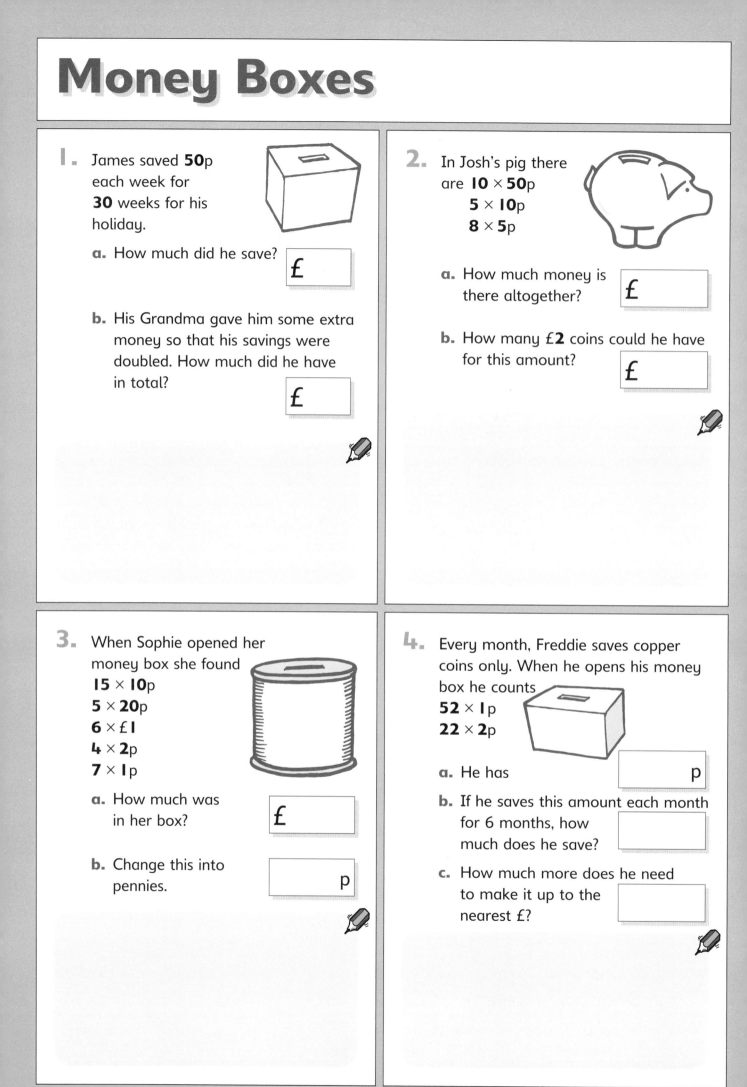

1. James saved **50**p each week for **30** weeks for his holiday.

  a. How much did he save? £ _____

  b. His Grandma gave him some extra money so that his savings were doubled. How much did he have in total? £ _____

2. In Josh's pig there are **10 × 50**p
     5 × 10p
     8 × 5p

  a. How much money is there altogether? £ _____

  b. How many £2 coins could he have for this amount? £ _____

3. When Sophie opened her money box she found
  15 × 10p
  5 × 20p
  6 × £1
  4 × 2p
  7 × 1p

  a. How much was in her box? £ _____

  b. Change this into pennies. _____ p

4. Every month, Freddie saves copper coins only. When he opens his money box he counts
  52 × 1p
  22 × 2p

  a. He has _____ p

  b. If he saves this amount each month for 6 months, how much does he save? _____

  c. How much more does he need to make it up to the nearest £? _____

18

Stage Shop

90p

£1·80

60p

50p

£2·00

£1·00

80p

Everyone is excited about the Fancy Dress Party. They go to the Stage Shop to buy one or two things. **Write out their bills and add them up.**

1. Marcus bought

Marcus' Bill

Stetson	£2·00
Wig	+ £1·00
Total	

In total he spent ☐

2. Emily bought

Emily's Bill

In total she spent ☐

3. Isabelle bought

Isabelle's Bill

In total she spent ☐

4. What would you buy?

Write your bill

My Bill

I spent ☐

Traffic

This graph shows the number of vehicles passing the school gate between 12 o'clock and 1 o'clock for 5 days.

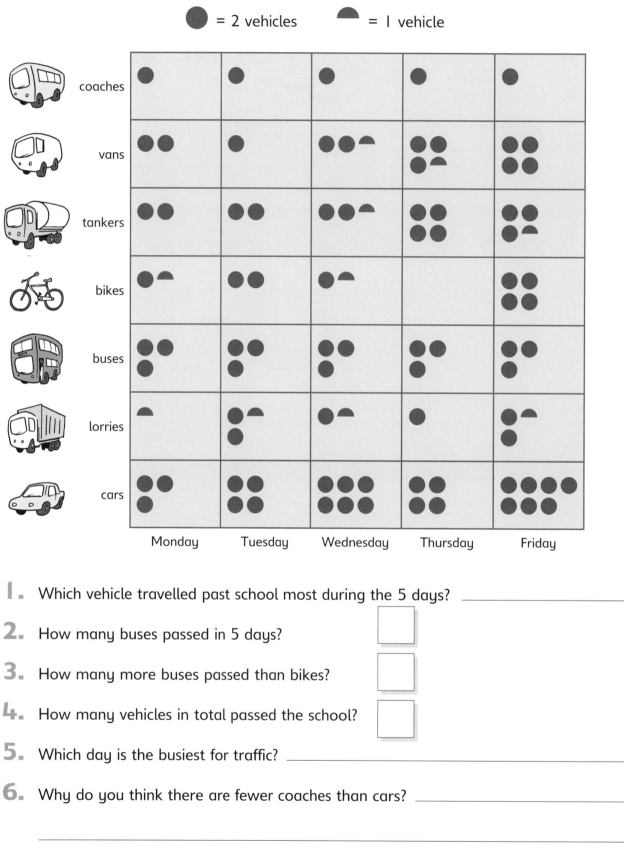

1. Which vehicle travelled past school most during the 5 days? _____

2. How many buses passed in 5 days? ☐

3. How many more buses passed than bikes? ☐

4. How many vehicles in total passed the school? ☐

5. Which day is the busiest for traffic? _____

6. Why do you think there are fewer coaches than cars? _____

_____

7. If it was snowing which vehicle that isn't on the graph might you see? _____

1. **a.** Work out the missing numbers in these magic squares.
Remember each row, each column and each diagonal add to the same number.

25	31	22
	26	29

12		10
	13	
		14

b. Can you work out a magic square for yourself?

2. Make the **3** sides of the triangle add up to **19**.

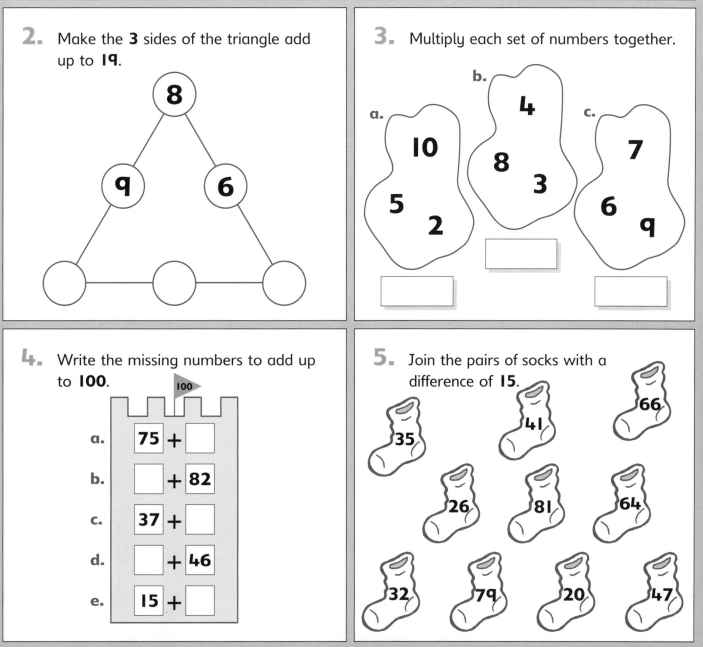

3. Multiply each set of numbers together.

a. 10 5 2

b. 4 8 3

c. 7 6 9

4. Write the missing numbers to add up to **100**.

100

a. 75 + ☐

b. ☐ + 82

c. 37 + ☐

d. ☐ + 46

e. 15 + ☐

5. Join the pairs of socks with a difference of **15**.

35 41 66

26 81 64

32 79 20 47

TV Times

MONDAY		TUESDAY	
10.30	TV Babes	2.00	Rumbles
11.00	Winnie the Pooh	2.25	Weather
11.10	Robert the Robot	2.30	The Jolleys
11.20	The Big Blue Bus	3.00	Sophie and Sam
11.30	Robin Hood	3.15	The Tinkers
1.00	News	3.40	Newsround

1. Write the names of Monday's programmes underneath the times they started.

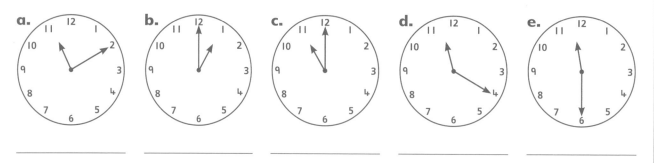

a.   b.   c.   d.   e.

_____   _____   _____   _____   _____

_____   _____   _____   _____   _____

2. How long do these programmes last?

a. The Jolleys _____

b. Rumbles _____

c. Robert the Robot _____

d. Robin Hood _____

e. Weather _____

f. The Tinkers _____

g. TV Babes _____

h. Sophie and Sam _____

3. Ashir watched **2** programmes for a total of **50** minutes. What did he watch?

_____

4. Anna watched for **15** minutes and then for **25** minutes. What did she watch?

_____

5. Freddie watched Robin Hood on Monday and The Jolleys on Tuesday?
How long did he watch TV? _____

6. Write on the clocks the times these programmes finish.

a. **b.** **c.** **d.** **e.**

The Tinkers   Rumbles   Sophie and Sam   The Jolleys   Weather

7. If you were allowed to watch some of these programmes for **1** hour **30** minutes, which would you choose?

_____

_____

8. **a.** Which is your favourite programme on TV?

_____

b. Which day is it shown?

_____

c. What time does it start?

d. When does it finish?

e. How long does it last? _____

Rajeev's Party

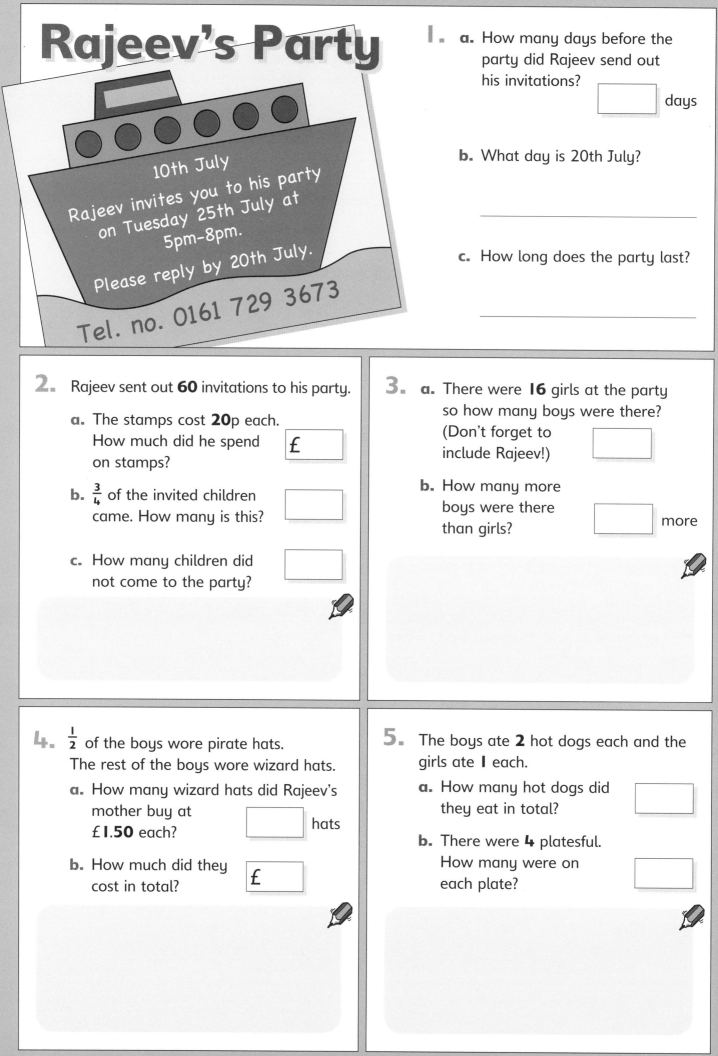

10th July

Rajeev invites you to his party on Tuesday 25th July at 5pm–8pm.

Please reply by 20th July.

Tel. no. 0161 729 3673

1. a. How many days before the party did Rajeev send out his invitations?

[ ] days

b. What day is 20th July?

_____

c. How long does the party last?

_____

2. Rajeev sent out **60** invitations to his party.

a. The stamps cost **20**p each. How much did he spend on stamps?

£[ ]

b. $\frac{3}{4}$ of the invited children came. How many is this?

[ ]

c. How many children did not come to the party?

[ ]

3. a. There were **16** girls at the party so how many boys were there? (Don't forget to include Rajeev!)

[ ]

b. How many more boys were there than girls?

[ ] more

4. $\frac{1}{2}$ of the boys wore pirate hats. The rest of the boys wore wizard hats.

a. How many wizard hats did Rajeev's mother buy at £**1.50** each?

[ ] hats

b. How much did they cost in total?

£[ ]

5. The boys ate **2** hot dogs each and the girls ate **1** each.

a. How many hot dogs did they eat in total?

[ ]

b. There were **4** platesful. How many were on each plate?

[ ]

6. Name the shapes used to make these hats.

_____ _____

_____ _____

7. Draw the lines of symmetry.

8. The party started at **5** o'clock and the disco began one hour later. The conjuror arrived **1½** hours after the disco started and performed his magic for **20** minutes. What time did he finish?

_____

9. At the disco all the girls were dancing but only **8** boys joined in. If double the number of boys had danced, how many children would have been dancing?

[   ] children

10. Rajeev blew out the **8** candles on his cake but they were magic candles which relit themselves. This happened **3** times before Rajeev realised. How many candles did he try to blow out?

[   ] candles

11. Later, they enjoyed fireworks. There were **15** rockets and twice as many fountains. Each child had a sparkler. How many fireworks were there altogether?

There were [   ] fireworks

Goals! Goals! Goals!

The number of goals scored by the school football team for $\frac{1}{2}$ a term are given below:

week **1 → 3**	week **3 → 6**	week **5 → 6**
week **2 → 1**	week **4 → 7**	week **6 → 9**

Use this data to complete the graph.

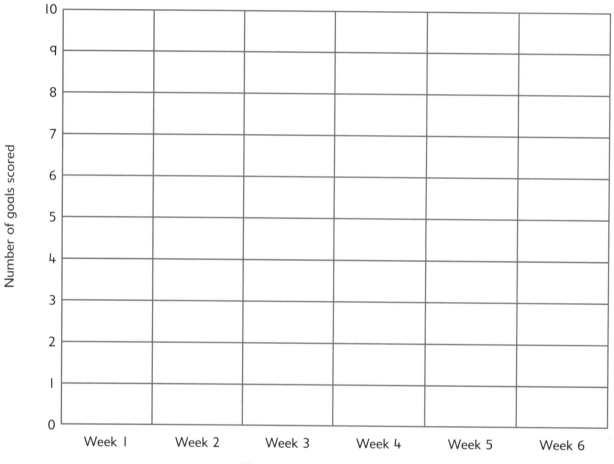

Number of goals scored

Number of weeks in half a term

Find out

1. Which week did the team score the least number of goals? _____

2. Which week did the team score the most goals? _____

3. Which **2** weeks did they score the same number of goals? _____

4. How many more goals were scored on week **4** than week **2**? _____

5. Which week did they score **2** more than the least number? _____

6. What was the total number of goals scored in weeks **4** and **6**? _____

7. What was the total number of goals scored in all the half-term? _____

Shape

1. What is a flat shape with **6** sides called?

_____

Draw one.

2. Name **2** shapes with **4** right angles.

_____

_____

How many right angles would there be in total?

There would be [ ] right angles.

3. How many rectangles can you count?

[ ] rectangles

4. What is a flat shape with **8** sides called?

_____

Draw one.

5. How many squares can you see?

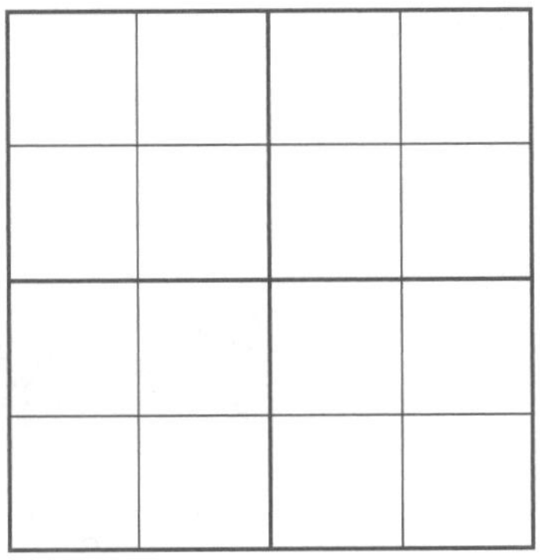

[ ] squares

6. How many triangles can you see?

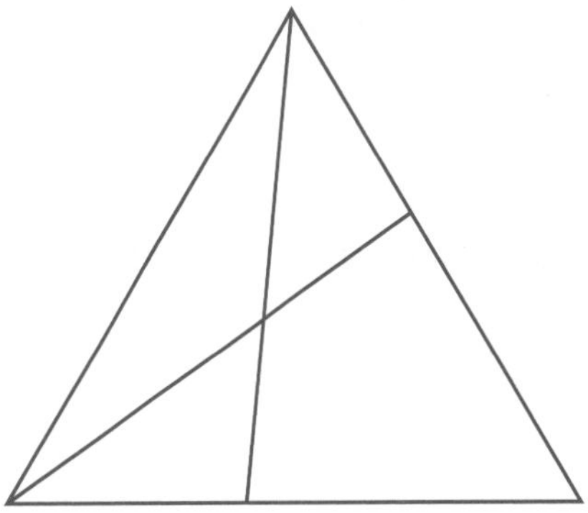

[ ] triangles

Schofield & Sims

the long-established educational publisher specialising in maths, English and science

Key Stage 2 Problem Solving is a series of graded activity books helping children to sharpen their mathematical skills. It encourages them to apply their maths skills to a range of 'real-life' situations, such as shopping and keeping score in games.

Key Stage 2 Problem Solving Book 1 covers:

- Equations
- Multiples of 2, 3, 4, 5, 6 and 10
- Lines of symmetry
- Counting money, recognising coins to £1 and calculating change
- Data handling
- Height/length/distance/capacity/time.

This book is suitable for children in Key Stage 2 – particularly those in Years 3 and 4.

The full range of titles in the series is as follows:

Key Stage 2 Problem Solving Book 1 (for Years 3 and 4)   ISBN 978 07217 0935 2

Key Stage 2 Problem Solving Book 2 (for Years 4 and 5)   ISBN 978 07217 0936 9

Key Stage 2 Problem Solving Book 3 (for Years 5 and 6)   ISBN 978 07217 0937 6

Key Stage 2 Problem Solving Book 4 (for Year 6)   ISBN 978 07217 1138 6

Have you tried **Mental Arithmetic** by Schofield & Sims?
This series helps children to sharpen their calculation skills by using mathematical knowledge to solve one- and two-step number problems.

**For further information and to place your order visit
www.schofieldandsims.co.uk or telephone 01484 607080**

ISBN 978 07217 0935 2

£3.50
(Retail price)

Key Stage 2

Age range 7-11 years

ISBN 978-07217-0935-2

9 780721 709352

Schofield & Sims

Dogley Mill, Fenay Bridge, Huddersfield HD8 0NQ
Phone: 01484 607080 Facsimile: 01484 606815
E-mail: sales@schofieldandsims.co.uk
www.schofieldandsims.co.uk